Who Can Build?

by Miriam Sklar

ISBN: 978-1-338-75089-8
Illustrated by John Lund

Published by Scholastic Inc., 557 Broadway, New York, NY 10012

10 9 8 7 6 5 4 68 25 26 27/0

Printed in Jiaxing, China. First printing, January 2021.

Birds can build.

Beavers can build.

Bees can build.

Ants can build.

Spiders can build.

Squirrels can build.

I can build!